ANIMAL SQUAT
the adventures of the wild things

written and illustrated by
DOUBLEWHY

Special thanks to Bess Komentarza and to
Vyvian Raoul – without you this book would
never have existed.

Dedicated to all the squat-mates in London.

First published in London, 2019 by Dog Section Press
Printed by Calverts Ltd., a workers' cooperative

ISBN 9781916036505

Dog Section Press logo by Marco Bevilacqua

Once upon a time there was a
bunch of wild and peculiar animals.

For one reason or another, they had
all run away from their owners, and
had decided they would no longer
accept anybody's rules or the idea
of ownership itself.

They no longer had any masters
and were determined that they
never would again.

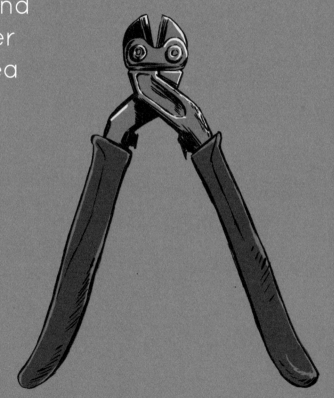

The wild creatures were free now,
but they still needed a home.

One night while romping about
they spotted an abandoned sugar
factory. They jumped the fence,
forced the lock of the back-door
with a crowbar, and got in!

They declared the sugar factory
their new den.

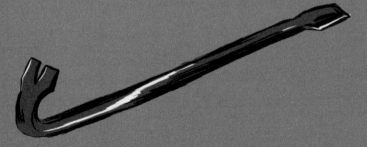

Despite what their former master thought, these wild creatures had some sense about them. So, first of all, they barricaded the doors.

A barricade is a way to protect an entrance or á passage by using scrap materials and rotten things. They created complicated and secret manoeuvres to open and close the entrance. Friends and random creatures were always welcome – but masters and warders beware!

The building was big enough for everyone to have their own room, and there was a big common space, where they sat to eat and organise events.

Living in such a building meant every day was a day for exploring and discovering. It was fun to find new uses for old objects that had been left to the dust.

The crew was made up of different kinds of animals: one was an artist and drag-queen; another was a one-legged book-fanatic; one was an anarchist computer hacker; one was a transsexual eco-activist; another was a full-time feminist, part-time model.

There were more who joined in, while some of them left to travel.

They didn't necessarily have much in common except for not letting each other feel ashamed or afraid of being what they wanted to be.

Nobody in the crew had an owner anymore, and they didn't make any money. But the amount of food that was thrown away every day by the supermarkets all over the city was more than enough to satisfy even the wildest appetites.

They would cycle around to find food that was recenlty thrown out, which wasn't even past the sell-by date and still sealed in its plastic wrappings. Otherwise it would just have been wasted.

Surprise! The night of the most marvelous, sparkling party arrived.

Howling music could be heard for miles and miles around the sugar factory. Wild creatures from all over the land attended, each one bringing their own sound. Thunder, rainbows, glitter and cotton candy everywhere!

Even the narrator got caught in the party's whirlwind and stopped writing to enjoy the cabaret.

Maybe a neighbour didn't appreciate the music. Maybe some stuck-up resident didn't approve of the smell that, for a while now, was coming from the sugar factory. The wild creatures never figured out why, but they found themselves in front of a strange creature they had never seen before.

Except for a red nose, it looked like a clown – yet it wasn't really funny at all. It called itself a judge – and made the wild things call it "your Honour" – while it was pointing a long, skinny, white finger at them.

Not much time passed before the police and bailiffs came, to protect the property of the owner – even though the owner had abandoned it.

What an unpleasant scene! They kicked the wild things out of the place they had made into their home.

All the work they had done to make the factory a warm, livible place was lost, and all the creatures' stuff was scattered on the sidewalk.

ICE

There wasn't much that they could say or do about this injustice. Still, Violet the Fox found a way to to get her point across.

They were in the street once again,
paying the price of freedom with the
discomfort of instability.

But wild things don't give up! And there are
so many empty buildings in this city. So here
they go again, scouting for a new building to
crack and transform into their home.

Don't they ever get tired? Indeed they do.
But they prefer this kind of tiredness to the
one that comes from working all day to
make someone else's wealth grow. They
don't even care about wealth at all. All they
want to do is to take the time and space to
be what they are: wild things!

YOU CAN WRITE ON THIS WALL!

DOG SECTION PRESS